FRANK ASCH

The Earth and I

Voyager Books • Harcourt, Inc.

Orlando   Austin   New York   San Diego   London

For information about permission to reproduce selections from this book, write to
trade.permissions@hmhco.com or to Permissions, Houghton Mifflin Harcourt
Publishing Company, 3 Park Avenue, 19th Floor, New York, New York 10016.

www.hmhco.com

First Voyager Books edition 2008

Voyager Books is a trademark of Harcourt, Inc., registered in the
United States of America and/or other jurisdictions.

The Library of Congress has cataloged the hardcover edition as follows:
Asch, Frank.
The earth and I/Frank Asch.
p.   cm.
Summary: A child explains how he and the Earth
dance and sing together and take turns listening to each other.
[1. Earth—Fiction.]   I. Title.
PZ7.A778Ear   1994
E—dc20   93-237
ISBN 978-0-15-200443-9
ISBN 978-0-15-206395-5 pb

SCP   20 19 18 17
4500762032

Printed in China

The paintings in this book were done in watercolors, acrylics,
and colored pencils on Arches watercolor paper, series 500.
The display type was set in Billy.
The text type was set in Columbus.
Color separations by Bright Arts, Ltd., Singapore
Printed and bound by RR Donnelley
Production supervision by Christine Witnik
Designed by Trina Stahl and Lori J. McThomas

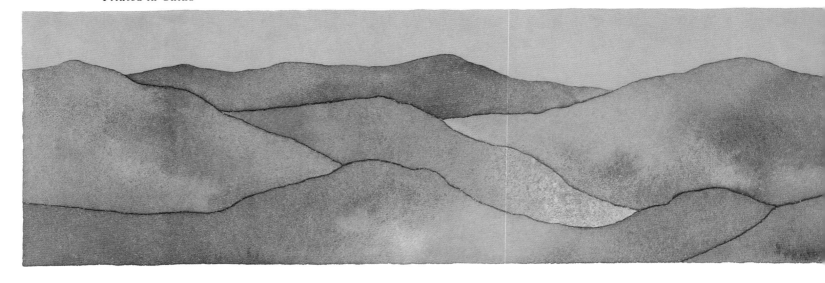

for Lynne and Eric

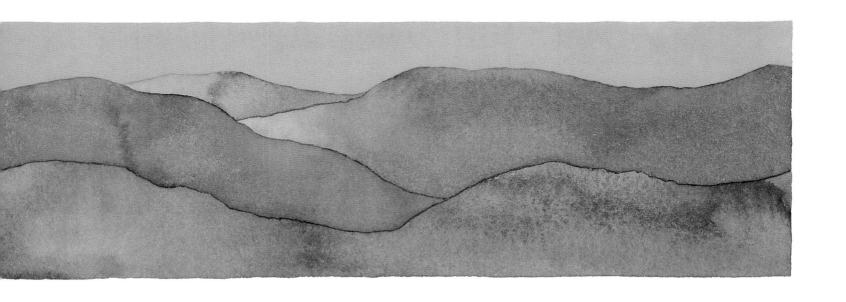

The Earth and I are friends.

Sometimes we go for long walks together.

I tell her what's on my mind.

She listens to every word.

Then I listen to her.

The Earth and I are friends.

We play together in my backyard.

I help her to grow.

She helps me to grow.

I sing for her.

She sings for me.

I dance for her.

She dances for me.

When she's sad,

I'm sad.

When she's happy,

I'm happy.

The Earth and I are friends.